Get Set, Go

by Nuala White

illustrated by Linda Bittner

Target Skill Short *Ee/e/*
High-Frequency Words *here, go, from*

PEARSON

Scott Foresman

Ben and Mom get set to go.

They get in the cab.

Ben and Mom see Dad.

Ben and Mom look at Dad.

Dad tells the cab to go.

We go from here to the Big Dig Spot.

Get set, go!

The cab gets to the Big Dig Spot.
Can you see it?

Look here, Ben. You can dig.
You can dig and dig and dig.
Get set, go!

Did you get one, Ben?

Dig, Ben, dig.

Look! Ben can get one.

Ben, Mom, and Dad get set
to dig and dig.
Get set, go!